ACE and KAT AT THE A TO Z STORE

Written by
Denise Heyl McEvoy
Illustrated by
Alistar

Ace wants to go shopping.
"What do you need to buy?" asks Kat.

"I don't remember," says Ace. "I'll know it
when I see it."

ALPHABETTY'S

A TO Z STORE

OPEN

At
ALPHABETTY'S
A TO Z
STORE,
it's easy to find what
you're shopping for.
We arrange everything
ALPHABETICALLY
Our departments go
from **A TO Z.**

Find the letters in the picture.

3

In the first department are things that start with A and B. There are anchors and aprons. There are bikes and beach balls. Ace doesn't see anything he needs.

Kat finds some boots. She puts them in her basket.

BEAUTIFUL!

Find things that start with the letter B.

Next, Ace looks at things that start with C and D. He doesn't need a canoe, a drum, or a cow costume. He definitely doesn't need a dress!

Kat finds a diamond collar.

C
D

DIVINE!

Find things that start with the letter D.

Ace checks the EFG department. He's not looking for eggs or gardening gloves. He doesn't need a fan or an easel or a globe.

Kat grabs a guitar.

GROOVY!

Find things that start with the letter G.

"I think I lost something," says Ace. "Was it my jacket?"

"You are wearing your jacket," Kat replies.

Ace knows he did not lose an igloo, a jack-in-the-box, or a helicopter.

Kat is hungry. She gets some ice cream.

Find things that start with the letter J.

11

Ace is sure he did not lose a kayak, a mailbox, a ladder, or a monkey mask. He wonders if he lost his keys.

Kat is thirsty. She gets some lemonade.

"I don't think I could lose a piano," Ace says.
He looks at the oranges, puppets, and notebooks.
"Did I lose my notebook?" he asks.

"No," sighs Kat. "Your notebook is in
your pocket."

Kat needs a nap. She gets a pillow.

Find things that start with the letter P.

15

Ace knows he did not lose a robot, a quail, or a surfboard.

"Maybe I lost my sunglasses," he says.

Kat finds a quilt. She curls up on a sofa and takes a quick snooze.

SALE

Find things that start with the letter S.

Ace looks at the television, violin, and ukelele. He is tired.

But Kat feels great! She tries on a tutu.

TOO, TOO TERRIFIC!

T U V

Find things that start with the letter T.

Ace is worried. WXYZ is the last department.
He doesn't need a yo-yo, x-ray goggles, or a wig.

Kat tries to fit a xylophone into her basket.

Find things that start with the letter W.

Kat gets a wheelbarrow. She takes out her wallet.

"That's it!" exclaims Ace. "I lost my wallet."

W X Y Z

YAHOO

X-RAY GOGGLES

Then Ace remembers ... all his money was in his wallet!

Find things that start with the letter Y.

So Kat buys a wallet for Ace ...
plus a few things for herself.